The Baby
in the Bulrushes
The Story of Moses

ISBN 1-84135-361-2

Copyright © 2005 Award Publications Limited

First published 2005

Published by Award Publications Limited,
27 Longford Street, London NW1 3DZ

Printed in China

The Baby in the Bulrushes

The Story of Moses

by Jackie Andrews
Illustrated by Roger de Klerk

AWARD PUBLICATIONS LIMITED

At one time, God's chosen people – the Hebrews – lived happily in Egypt. But then the king of Egypt ordered his soldiers to kill all the Hebrew baby boys.

One mother hid her baby in a basket among the bulrushes in the river, so the soldiers would not find him.

The king's daughter went down to the river to bathe and heard the baby crying. She found the basket and decided to keep the baby herself, and called him Moses.

The princess needed someone to look after the baby for her. His own mother offered to take care of him, so Moses grew up among his own family.

The cruel king made slaves of all the
Hebrews and made them work hard for him.

But the young Moses went to live in the palace with the princess and was taught to read and write with the other royal children.

When Moses had grown up and moved away from Egypt, God spoke to him one day from a burning bush.

"My people are suffering," he said. "I want you to go back to Egypt and rescue them."

Moses was afraid. "Suppose they won't listen to me?"

"Don't worry," said God. "I will help you."

Moses went back to the king of Egypt and asked him to release the Hebrew slaves. The king refused. Instead, he made them all work harder.

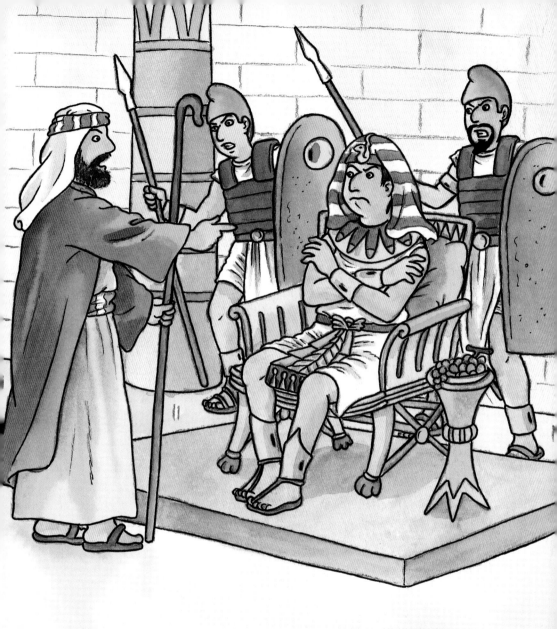

"Because you are so stubborn," said Moses, "God will punish you. Egypt will suffer nine different disasters."

First the river turned to blood, killing all the fish. Then the country was overrun with frogs, flies, disease and sickness.

Hailstorms flattened the crops. Locusts ate everything green. Darkness covered the land for three days. But still the king refused to free his slaves.

The last disaster was the worst of all. God's angels flew over the land and took the lives of all the first-born Egyptian children and animals, including the king's own son.

Only then did the king agree to let the
Hebrews go.

Moses led God's people out into the desert to look for a new home. The king's soldiers chased after them, but God kept them safe.

He also gave them food and water, and a
pillar of cloud to guide them by day. At night,
they followed a pillar of fire.

Moses was chosen by God to be a guide and teacher of his chosen people.

He gave Moses the Ten Commandments, to show everyone how he wanted them to live their lives and worship him. Many people still try to follow them today.